NO HANDS

C000044190

in celebration of feet

Gerry Pyves

Shi'Zen Publications

Published by Shi'Zen Publications
PO Box 57, Hebden Bridge, W.Yorks, HX7 6WW
+44 (0) 870 – 24 - 30 - 876
www.shizen.co.uk

drawings and layout by John Coombes
cover photos by Stephen Lord
printed in Great Britain by The Charlesworth Group, Huddersfield
ISBN 0 9539 0742 – 2

DEDICATION

There is only one dedication possible for a book about the reflexes of the feet.

Eunice Ingham

Has any single person given more to the natural healing community? I think not. This book is offered only as a side note to that woman's amazingly generous gift to humanity – a method of cure based on simple massage to the feet.

Her two books are not only perfect expositions of her technique, but also perfect expositions of the naturopathic approach to healing. Do not be misled by the simplicity of her style – everything you need to know about natural approaches to healing can be found in the pages of her books.

It is my belief that everything that needs to be said about Reflexology has been said by this giant of a woman – and in her generosity she has gifted it to us. All that is left is to go out there, and stimulate those reflexes!

This book seeks to add the new approach of NO HANDS to the service of this lady's great work and the work of Reflexologists across the world. It adds nothing to this lady's great naturopathic approach and teachings.

ACKNOWLEDGMENTS

Putting together a book like this is a real team effort.

First, comes learning the Bodywork itself. In the three years before I got injured I was gifted three great teachers:

I learned the power of touch itself through a profoundly gifted Swedish Massage trainer and Mind-Body specialist - thank you Ron Rieck !

I learned about energy and the meridians from a deeply spiritual shiatsu teacher – thank you Sonia Moriceau!

I learned about the magic and wizardry of touch from the originator of Body Harmony – thank you Don McFarland!

And that is all the training I was able to do before I got injured. After my injury? I was too busy working away with my colleagues in my stroke laboratory in the Pennines of West Yorkshire to have time for anything else! The truth of the matter is I learned all that I really know about zero-strain and effective Bodywork from just one person – a person with over ten thousand different faces:

my client
always there
lying on the plinth
waiting for me to begin

And if you share with me this awesome journey of touch healing, then I hope with this gift of NO HANDS, to help you to continue your journey - free from all injury

Second, comes actually writing this book after so many years of talking about it! I wish to acknowledge the phenomenal support of Geraldine Scott. In my last book I called you 'the midwife'. How to acknowledge someone generous enough to sit at the other end of the phone for hours without complaint, all the while giving encouragement? I would have stumbled and fallen so many times but for you, Geraldine. Your wise and steady hand is written into every page. Thank you.

Thank you John Coombes for giving the lay out of this book the benefits of your outstanding artistic talent. The result is a book that says more about Bodywork in one drawing than can be said in volumes of words. Thank you Stephen Lord for your beautiful photographs and thank you Stephen Williamson for all your technical wizadry – Gandalf rides Middle Earth again!

And finally there is, once again, the continual understanding and necessary forgiveness from my family. It is a kind of disease, this writing and your daily acceptance of my very serious condition is written into every page. Thank you Francesca, Laurie, Hannah and Alfie.

CONTENTS

in celebration of feet

so
there is this therapy
called reflexology

proven by the thousands who have felt the healing power of its touch

can you resist it's calling?

it craves to touch
the part of your body that walks you through life
through every single event

it begs to celebrate,
for just one moment

the part of you
where every successful step
and every sorrowing failure
is recorded.

it begs to touch
it craves to celebrate

the part of you
upon which every joy
and every disappointment is imprinted.

it seeks to remind you
with the gentlest of murmurings

that each inhalation and exhalation of your breath
is felt through the very soles of your feet
and that each is rumoured to leave echoes therein…

and that this
is the part of you where
every confident movement
every faltering step

is unerringly etched
into the very fabric
of your tissue's memory.

yes, the foot records your every exaltation and every sorrow
how can your experiences not imprint upon your soles?

when you experience joy and elation,
do you not walk more lightly - with a spring upon this earth?

and when you sorrow
do not your steps tread more heavily?

yes, every experience you have felt is imprinted upon the soles of your feet.

so
there is this therapy
called reflexology…

proven by the thousands who have felt the healing power of its touch.

so much pressing and so much precision…
where the therapist says "come rest your feet,
and let me knead, pummel and anoint them"

where pressing the smallest part
can release whole continents of healing

who is insane enough to refuse such an invitation?

and it comes with such a pedigree!
when he, yes, even the great JC himself
knelt down and lovingly washed the feet
of his betrayer.

who can refuse such an invitation?

an invitation to one of the most revered

and spiritual of all therapies
spiritual by divine association…

so kick those shoes away - prison wardens to the feet!
and free your feet

feel the very soul of this earth
pulsating through your body!

and when you need that balm
which only touch can provide

then carry your feet to this altar
where your every tissue's memory
is honoured

so
there is this therapy
called reflexology

proven by the thousands who have felt the healing power of its touch.

can you resist its calling?

welcome to NO HANDS
in celebration of feet

This is the newest of all the NO HANDS revolutions. It is founded upon the same Postural Secrets that have utterly transformed the world of Therapeutic Massage and Chair Massage.

It is also informed by the very same natural principles of health propounded by Eunice Ingham, who delivered the gift that is Reflexology to this world. Saints have been made for contributing less than that great lady.

If you are a bodyworker who touches the feet, then it is my prayer that this book will take you another step further on your bodywork journey. You're the BAREFOOT DOCTORS of the modern era. In awe at the amazing work you do, I offer this as my gift to you. It is born out of love, passion and a profound belief in the infinite possibilities of healing through touch.

Namaste,

Gerry

INTRODUCTION

Following injury to both my wrists, I was forced to spend 15 years focusing entirely on the how of bodywork as opposed to the what. And I discovered that there were only seven secrets to bodywork mastery. Seven keys to unlock the door to bodywork heaven....

What started as a way to survive for me personally, became a way to help all practitioners protect their careers. It actually took many years before it dawned on me that this was also a fundamental re-write of every single principle of Swedish Massage that has been taught since Per Henrik Ling.

Over time, I began to realise that I had discovered a new bodywork technology - a technology that requires a quantum shift in every aspect of the practitioner's mind and body. Sometimes it felt as if I was listening to a great bodywork master whispering to me from a couple of miles away – if only I could listen harder! In all truth, I still cannot work out whether I am the student or the teacher. And, like the boy who saw that the emperor had no clothes on, I am forced to shout the obvious:

> "You know, what really affects bodywork
> is not the technique at all
> but
> *the way it is delivered!*"

How come so much of current bodywork training focuses on technique? In the classroom we cannot predict what outcome will result from certain movements. What every experienced bodyworker knows is that each client is unique. Each configuration of muscle tendon and tissue that we touch is a unique matrix that reflects perfectly the life of its owner...

What really matters is how we approach this person. It matters many times more than anything we do technically. How we breathe and think dictates every millimetre of our movement and controls every aspect of our effectiveness. So let us address this issue before we consider any techniques!

This brings us to the most important part of the healing equation: the Bodyworker. Now this is worth a thousand books, my friend. As surely as the stars pay homage to the unbelievable divinity of creation, the moving breath and soul's wisdom of the Bodyworker pays homage to the client's self-healing.

So, instead of spending all our time upon this puerile obsession called technique, we should focus upon learning the Seven Secrets. Seven Secrets that make our bodywork really sing….and help our clients dance their way into the great becoming.

Seven Secrets that focus exclusively, obsessively and crazily on Zen-like questions such as "where does the Massage stroke actually begin?". Questions that mean we can become like those crazy "mad for it" medieval philosophers who meditated on the number of Angels that could fit on the head of a pin. And like those mad medieval monks, we too can follow the line that leads us so close to the kingdom of divine touch, that we sense we are touching the very gates of heaven in our bodywork…

Yessir!

That is the touch for me!

BACKGROUND

THE SEVEN STAGES OF INJURY AND REFLEXOLOGY
The risk of injury to Reflexologists is arguably even greater than the risk to Massage Therapists

NO HANDS
As well as providing a zero-strain alternative to conventional Reflexology, NO HANDS prioritises homeostasis over diagnosis and proposes a 4-stage treatment protocol based on ancient Bodywork principles.

THE HISTORICAL REFLEX
The birth of Reflexology coincided with the mass production of the hard soled shoe.

THE POLITICAL REFLEX
Reflexology is a political act, concerning itself primarily with re-establishing our connection with the Earth.

THE MUSCULAR REFLEX
NO HANDS brings new possibilities for opening up the feet more deeply and more rapidly than ever before.

FOUR ZONES, SEVEN SURFACES AND ONE SOFT FRONT
As well as bringing the Seven Postural Secrets to the way a practitioner moves, NO HANDS brings a huge variety of contact surfaces that can be employed by the Reflexologist.

THE ALPHA STATE
The profoundly healing Alpha-state can be achieved in just a few moments with NO HANDS.

SEVEN STAGES OF INJURY & REFLEXOLOGY

The risk of injury to Reflexologists is arguably even greater than the risk to Massage therapists

Everything you need to know about injury and bodywork is contained in the appendix. Regarding Reflexology, almost every bodyworker I have met has confessed to me in private that the therapy that really added most to their injury problem was…

Reflexology

It employs a dangerous combination of repetition and pressure through the wrists and hands…a repetition that can create RSI – a condition almost unknown in Eunice Ingham's time. The necessarily 'held' and often rigid upper body posture of traditional Reflexology places great strain on the whole back, neck and shoulder girdle – no matter how well it is done. In addition to this, the frequent need for deep and incisive point-specific movements places enormous pressure on the fingers and thumbs. If the gentle tapping of a typist is said to produce 20 tonnes of pressure through her fingers each day, then what sort of tonnage might Reflexologists be putting through their hands?

There is no doubt that some can survive the repetition and pressure without injury. After all, there are many contributory factors to RSI. However, the simple truth is this: many Reflexologists who have a full time clinical practice become injured.

If ever there was a time for the application of the Seven Postural Secrets of NO HANDS to Reflexology, I believe it is now. The true story of Janet is one that I come across all too often…

JANET'S STORY

Janet Miller is a 54 year old practitioner from Knaresborough in North Yorkshire who was happy for me to tell her story and use her name. Four years back, she rang to ask me if I could help her shoulder problem by teaching her NO HANDS Massage. I explained that unfortunately, working without using the arms was a little 'left of field' even for me! Meanwhile, Janet was no longer seeing clients and no longer doing the work she loved.

When I probed further she explained how she had been fine doing massage for several years, but that her shoulder injury had started to develop whilst actually doing her Reflexology training. She was clearly a gifted and enthusiastic student and admits that she did twice as many case clients as anyone else on her course and loved the work.

When she rang me she was in tears at having to cancel all her clients. Nothing surprised me about her story – I had already heard it so many times before. But I cannot hear the story of a single practitioner being injured without feeling my own pain again. It was quite clear, in Janet's case that the added pressure and strain placed by her Reflexology work was "the straw that broke the camel's back".

There is a happy and rather surprising ending to this story. I invited Jane to attend a course "just to watch" – in order to give her some hope for the future. She had sounded so despondent over the phone that I wanted to help lift her spirits as well as give her a vision of the possibilities for the future. In the first lunch break she asked if I would let her join in as she thought that by moving in the way I prescribed she could avoid pain or injury. By applying the Seven Postural Secrets, she soon discovered that she could actually use her arms in a totally zero-strain way. She was very excited by how she could massage the feet without pain – this was in the very early days, before any NO HANDS reflex course.

The next day, this feisty 54 yr old returned to the course wearing hot-pants, announcing she was ready to do battle and reclaim her clients. To much laughter and joy from the rest of the group, she explained that she had been so inspired that she wanted to experiment with using the back of her thigh to massage us all – hence the hot pants! This in itself shows you something of the indomitable character of this woman!

By the end of this second day she had rung up some friends and arranged for them to come and try out this new massage. She was able to rebuild her practise, and when I spoke to her on the phone recently she said: "I only lost a couple of clients. Thanks to you Gerry, I am still able to practice - you saved my career and my life!". As far as I know, Janet is the only therapist in the UK who has rebuilt her career using the backs of her legs!

Janet has been practising ever since, and is one of the reasons for this book. Her spirit of giving and courage in the face of injury, pain and adversity has been an inspiration to me. To me, she represents the generous spirit of all Reflexologists.

NO HANDS

As well as providing a zero-strain alternative to conventional Reflexology, NO HANDS prioritises homeostasis over diagnosis and proposes a 4-stage treatment protocol based on ancient Bodywork principles.

My experience of NO HANDS and my growing understanding of the Seven Postural Secrets means I approach stimulating foot reflexes primarily as a Bodyworker, rather than a Reflexologist. My sole interest is in finding a clinically effective zero-strain way to deliver reflex stimulation to the foot.

Because of this simple agenda, I need not bother myself with arguments about this or that school of Reflexology – in fact I find such arguments detrimental to my health! In the direct and simple tradition of Eunice Ingham, I am simply looking at how to work the reflexes of the foot.

I believe that NO HANDS adds considerably to the overall picture of Reflexology in three distinct ways:

THE 3 CONTRIBUTIONS OF NO HANDS TO REFLEX STIMULATION

1. Zero-strain reflex stimulation. It does this by training therapists how to effortlessly work the reflexes of the foot utilising the Seven Postural Secrets. This means we can do the work of reflexology without any risk of injury to the practitioner. These same secrets also enable us to give some of the deepest massage ever experienced to the muscles of the foot. By opening the foot so powerfully and effectively, much of the work of Reflexology has been achieved before even a single reflex has been pressed. I believe that this opening up of the foot reveals the reflexes and makes them more easily accessible to the therapist. It also makes it more likely that everyday life will stimulate the client's reflexes naturally.

2. Whole foot reflex stimulation. The approach is simple. It seeks to stimulate as many of the reflexes in the foot as possible – through the introduction of some very powerful zero-strain methods. In this way, the therapist can effortlessly stimulate all the reflexes on the foot, whether tender or not. This approach thus prioritises the natural homeostasis of the body. The body takes whatever reflex stimulation it needs for its own self-healing. This approach does not preclude the practice of treating specific ailments with specific reflex point work.

3. 4-stage treatment protocol. NO HANDS introduces a 4-stage approach to reflex stimulation based on ancient bodywork principles. This is a pleasant and enjoyable treatment protocol that is getting some amazing clinical results – though it is still early days. This places the mental state of the client at the forefront of every treatment. It enables the client to speedily reach a state of total relaxation which, I believe, can help to open up the channels between the reflexes and their target organs.

THE HISTORICAL REFLEX

The birth of Reflexology coincided with the mass production of the hard soled shoe.

It is amazing how the history of our species is really the story of the human spirit continually seeking balance and homeostasis. The birth of factory produced shoes in the late nineteenth century, coincided with the 'discovery' of zone reflexes by the anaesthetist William Fitzgerald.

Mass production of shoes meant that for the first time people who bought shoes were buying them cheaply. It also meant that for the very first time, they were actually forced to fit their feet into pre-designed shapes. Prior to this, the shoe-maker would mould the shoe around each person's foot. From this point on, the foot was placed in a prison.

Modern clinical Reflexology as a therapy can only be said to have truly arrived with the work of Eunice Ingham in the early 1930's. Her genealogy can be traced through Joseph Riley directly to William Fitzgerald. Whatever the roots of Reflexology are it was only with Eunice Ingham's groundbreaking maps of the body's organs super-imposed upon the foot that Reflexology as a discreet therapy can be said to have arrived in the West.

Of course, there are many, much more ancient roots for the theory and practise of various kinds of reflex stimulation. From ancient Chinese, Egyptian and Vedic manuscripts we have many antecedents for the therapeutic benefits to be derived from the simple act of stimulating reflexive points on the feet.

Pressing one part of the body to have a therapeutic effect on other parts of the body is as ancient as Bodywork itself.

Eunice Ingham's Mediterranean and Oriental antecedents may be many, but it was her innovative genius in putting it all together that heralded the birth of Reflexology. For this reason I take the beginning of Reflexology to be in 1938 with the publication of her groundbreaking book "Stories that Feet can Tell" (Ingham Publishing).

What does this historical coincidence of the mass – produced hard soled shoe and Zone Theory teach us about the purpose and function of Reflexology? It is a therapy that appeared at precisely the time when our connection with the Earth had become massively disrupted for the very first time in the history of our species. Our 'Plug' into mother Earth, Gaia, the Source, whatever you call it, had been badly compromised.

Reflexology is a therapy that can help us to re-connect with our feet and therefore with the Earth. This reconnection is achieved through stimulating the reflexes in our feet. Anyone who has walked out of an effective Reflexology session delighting in the aliveness of sensation that can be felt in their feet knows this to be true.

THE POLITICAL REFLEX

Reflexology is a political act, concerning itself primarily with re-establishing our connection with the Earth.

Once we have a society where the feet are disconnected from the Earth – a society in shoes that is, then we have serious planetary trouble and an urgent need for Reflexology.

The birth of Reflexology as a popular mass-therapy is inconceivable without the birth of tarmac and the hard-soled shoe as created by western industrial society.

Modern imbalances result, in my opinion, from this disconnection from the Earth and the cessation of stimulation to our reflexes. Feeling all our movements against the Earth is our healing….

The purpose of Reflexology is nothing less than to re-forge our natural and ancient connection with the Earth.

It is no accident that the near destruction of one of the greatest "Earth-Connected" cultures on our planet, the American Indian, took place at the hands of a culture in which the shoe and the boot already dominated.

I believe that Reflexology actually redresses this dangerous imbalance and disconnection from the Earth, whether we intend it to or not.

This is how it has been since the beginning of time

Bare feet walking upon the Earth

Or with soft moccasins

Or hard clogs

Natural Earth, skin and wood.

This way, the foot is continually being opened, worked and stimulated by the wonderfully irregular surfaces of the uncovered Earth.

Ancient people knew this and worshipped the healing power of the Earth accordingly.

Then came tarmac and asphalt and

Shoes....

Heralding the end of this natural stimulation of the foot's reflexes

Heralding an end to the natural Shi'Zen provided by the Earth's surface

MUSCULAR REFLEXOLOGY

NO HANDS brings new possibilities for opening up the feet more deeply and more rapidly than ever before.

It is about bringing the reflexes so close to the surface of the foot that everyday movements once again trigger the body's own self-healing mechanisms – even in the shoe! And it is about encouraging our clients to take off their shoes wherever possible.

Do you really need your shoes whilst reading this? If not, take 'em off! Press your feet against something uneven…

With NO HANDS, we re-educate the client to the Earth by providing extremely deep massage to all the muscles of the foot. So that even if we forget to press or miss a single tender reflex, the client walks out of the session and gets a treatment anyway – from the Earth.

This amount of deep, relaxing pressure is only possible as a result of the discovery of NO HANDS massage. Any practitioner trying to apply this much pressure through their hands and wrists will get injured. Any client who experiences this amount of pressure through the practitioner's relatively sharp and bony hands will experience discomfort and pain. Without a full understanding of the Postural Secret of FALLING (see next section) such pressure is dangerous to both client and therapist alike.

The voluntary muscles of the feet seem to protect the reflexes just as effectively as the voluntary muscles of the spine protect the tsubos of the bladder meridian. There is a pattern, here. Muscles protect reflexes and place our healing under mental voluntary control. This is why it is so important to address the mental state of our clients as well as their physical state. So, if you had the opportunity to give the deepest foot massage possible and awaken every reflex in the foot gently, would that add to your Bodywork?

One of the reasons that people are calling NO HANDS the 'Gentle Giant' of bodywork is because practitioners have all the power of their whole bodyweight, gravity and the biggest muscles of the body at their disposal. This power is then used gently, without any pain or discomfort to the client whatsoever.

a Gentle Giant

Mmmm….who would you most like your Bodywork from?

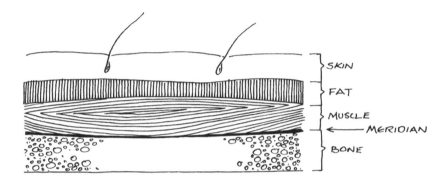

"The voluntary muscles of the feet seem to protect the reflexes just as effectively as the voluntary muscles of the spine protect the tsubos of the bladder meridian"

FOUR ZONES, SEVEN SURFACES AND ONE SOFT FRONT

As well as bringing the Seven Postural Secrets to the way a practitioner moves, NO HANDS brings a huge variety of contact surfaces that can be employed by the Reflexologist.

There are four zones available to every Bodyworker. These consist of: the hand (Primary Zone), the forearm (Secondary Zone), the upper arm (Tertiary Zone) and the rest of the body (Quarterly Zone). Each zone has a wide variety of surfaces and prominences that can be used in Bodywork.

Most NO HANDS is delivered through the Soft Front and other surfaces of the Secondary Zone. This Soft Front can be found on the proximal anterior surface, just an inch above the medial epicondyle. Many reflexes will be stimulated by this Soft Front simply because so much pressure can be applied painlessly to the client's muscles. This phenomenal pressure releases tension from the foot and opens up the reflexes almost magically. The end result is reflex stimulation, because:

An open, relaxed and soft foot is a foot where the reflexes are firing and receiving stimulation all the time – just as nature intended.

When we need a little more point-specific pressure, however, we can satisfactorily employ the ulna edge and the small hooks of the styloid process as well as the elbow itself. These long bones and their ends are so much more robust than the spongy, cancellous bones of the hand and wrist and are less prone to injury.

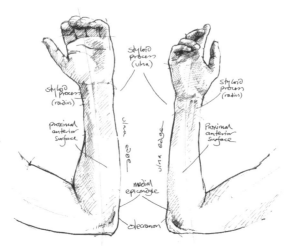

THE ALPHA STATE

The profoundly healing Alpha-state can be achieved in just a few moments with the 4-stage treatment protocol.

Reflexology already works worldwide. No doubts about this one. Thanks to the life-time's dedication of one woman and the thousands that she inspired.

What NO HANDS can add to this amazing approach is the means to create some very deep and relaxing effects for the client. I believe that this can increase the effectiveness of each treatment.

In just a few minutes it is now possible to bring the client into that very special and deep state of relaxation that all Bodyworkers know. We normally associate this state with the Alpha brain-wave pattern. This is the state in which the client is not asleep, but is drifting on the edge of consciousness and where many of the self-healing systems of the body kick in. Much gurgling of gastric juices is heard as the autonomic system kicks in and the intestinal muscles relax. Some call it the dream world where true healing begins…rarely is this achieved in less than 20 minutes. With NO HANDS the client drops into it almost immediately – as if by magic!

The reason for this, I believe, is the combination of immense power and great gentleness that is now available. Technically, this is achieved by the unique combination of the practitioner's bodyweight FALLING into the client's tissues and the use of the Soft Front of the practitioner's arms. Great Power. Great Gentleness.

With this new development, it became essential to look at conventional treatment protocols and to see how NO HANDS could support the proven effectiveness of Reflexology. As a result, I now offer my 4-stage treatment protocol to the profession.

This approach progresses from a Systemic Release of the whole body, to Leg Muscle Release, to Foot Muscle Release and finally to specific Reflex Point Release. It can be achieved in both supine and prone positions for the client. As will become clear later on in this book, it is only at stage four, Reflex Point Release that we attempt to stimulate the actual reflex points.

The effect this approach has on both mind and body is truly astounding. The extra time spent on the first three stages pays dividends in a reduction of treatment time needed for the final stage. Once clients are doing the healing work themselves, there is so much less to do…

SEVEN POSTURAL SECRETS

At the very heart of the revolution that is NO HANDS lie the Seven Postural Secrets.

I call them secrets because if they were not secrets every school in the land would be teaching them…

What makes bodywork really sing, is not the techniques we use, but the manner in which we use them

The Seven Postural Secrets remain the key to all effective bodywork

Observation of any Bodywork Master will show at least five of these Postural Secrets operative at any one moment. They are:

HARA

SOLE

FLOW

FALLING

KNEELING

SUPPORT

SHIRE HORSE

HARA

The belly of the Buddha. The energetic and postural centre of the body. The place from which all our charisma emanates. The seat of all our power and the place of instinct and intuition.

Mostly we use HARA as a way of getting out of our heads and being guided by our 'gut feelings'. The breath is central to opening and engaging this centre. We visualise the hands and arms as just extensions of the HARA.

Imagine walking around the room with a gravid belly that is so heavy it makes your knees begin to buckle. That is HARA – walking. The HARA likes to do things slowly, with breath and with connection to self.

HARA is at the centre of every single NO HANDS movement and is at the centre of our mental focus. Every single mssage movement we make has it's conception deep within the HARA.

Moving and breathing from your HARA will reward you with many moments of magic and transformation.

Look at this drawing of the 'foot mangle', aimed at releasing tension in the foot. Can you feel how this movement comes, not from the arms, but straight from the practitioner's HARA?

SOLE

Through the SOLE of your foot, you gain the nourishment necessary to give truly powerful bodywork. Like the roots of a tree, the soles of your feet spread tentacles deep into the floor…

If conception of the massage stroke takes place within the HARA, then the stroke's gestation takes place in the SOLE. The energy of each stroke goes with your weight. This drops down into the earth before it becomes anything to do with the client. For Reflexologists this has an added significance, because it shows you how to walk the talk by feeling the soles of your own feet even as you give a treatment.

TRY THIS NOW:
Stand in the middle of the room, barefoot. Let your HARA sink down into your feet – let them soften and open as you drop down. Just the same as in the drawing. Your HARA can initiate movement and you experience this as a change of pressure between your SOLE and the ground upon which you stand. Now, very slowly you move an arm or a hand. Slowly enough to feel the change in pressure on your feet as you move. Every movement you make with your hands or your head can be felt through the soles of your feet. Your feet become pressure plates that register the slightest movement in your body.. By sinking your HARA over specific points of each foot you can provide pin-point stimulation of each reflex point on the SOLE. Do this every day to stimulate the reflexes on the sole of your foot.

SOLE is about focusing your awareness on feeling everything you do through your feet. Such Earth connection is both empowering and protective.

Look at the drawing on the opposite page. SOLE is where everything is felt. The practice of SOLE will enable your every stroke to be fed and powered from the Earth. Such a connection to the SOLE of each foot and to the Earth is how you can 'walk the talk' of Reflexology.

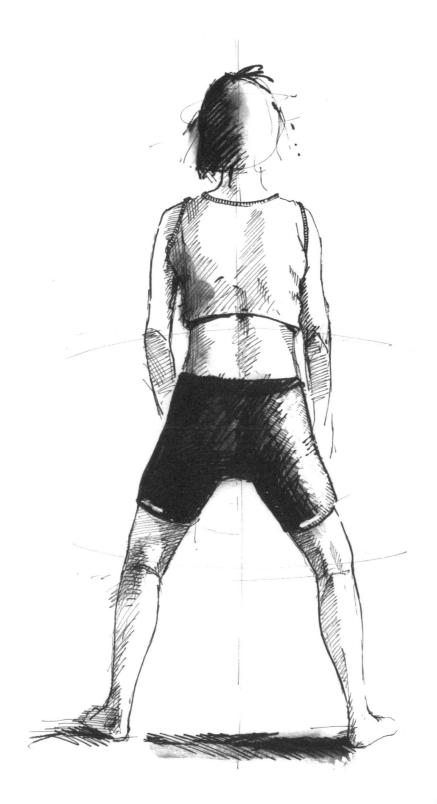

FLOW

The massage stroke can be said to truly have it's birth through FLOW. From its beginnings in the HARA and then its gestation in the earth and your SOLE, the stroke actually manifests itself through FLOW.

Imagine a room full of therapists who are moving very slowly with gravid bellies, feeling every nuance of their movement through the soles of their feet and doing "Air Massage", looking for all the world like a room of Tai – Chi masters, or dancing bears! This is a regular sight at all NO HANDS trainings.

FLOW is about the postural perfection of continuous movement. It is where the dancer within each bodyworker lives. It is about connecting with the flow of energy and fluid within our own bodies and also within our clients. It is about creating and channelling whole vortices of energy – harnessing the elemental power of the tornado. Wizards knew all about this…

FLOW is where the poet meets the scientist. Force and pressure are no longer necessary, because FLOW will shape the bodywork just like the sea shapes the solid rock into beautiful cliffs. In the same way that a tiny trickle of water shapes a whole valley. Effortless eternity.

Look at this drawing. It captures the power of FLOW superbly. Can you feel how HARA and SOLE contribute to the power of this movement? The practice of FLOW will bring an ability to work powerfully, continuously and effortlessly without tiring.

FALLING

Learning the art and science of FALLING is the bread and butter of NO HANDS. Impossible to put into words this one. It happened accidentally the very first time. I have spent the last 15 years understanding it – I believe I am getting close !

Here is the source of all the power and all the gentleness. Falling so that I can control the difference between 82% of my weight falling and 82.5% of my fallen weight – this is the greatest pre-occupation of all NO HANDS Bodyworkers.

This FALLING is so powerful that it alone warrants 100 years of research at the university of Bodywork! These are really just notes from a beginner…

Transferring my bodyweight into my client is how I control and manipulate energy.

That last sentence took 20 years to write and contains more information about bodywork than I can give you in even twenty days of training.

On a more nuts and bolts level FALLING is done in three distinct stages. First we fall, then we release the lower back and then we return to our start position by lowering our hips even further. Each stage is done without any strain.

Look at this drawing. Spend a moment meditating upon it's beauty. Feel the softness, the caring and the profound letting go – of the practitioner. Can you imagine what self healing such gentle profundity can create? For the Reflexologist, the practice of FALLING provides a power to each movement that is beyond pressure. This magical combination of movement, weight and mental awareness creates transformative bodywork, for both practitioner and client. It is a synergy of healing…

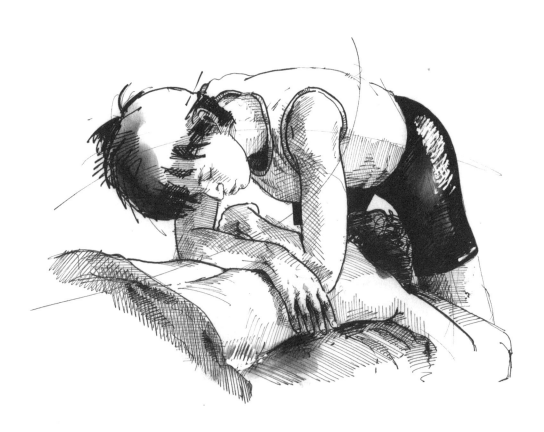

KNEELING

KNEELING is the only known way for a bodyworker to apply pressure or weight onto a client with an absolutely perfectly vertical spine. The discovery of KNEELING as a Bodywork principle will do more for the health of practitioners than the rest of NO HANDS put together.

In many ways KNEELING is like SOLE, only through the knees. It warrants especial mention because it is such a major part of NO HANDS. As someone who loves both fell and marathon running, I know there can be a problem with middle age and knees. This means that KNEELING has to be approached with considerable caution. In order to run I take great care of my knees.

Firstly, NO PAIN. This is practically a Postural Secret all of it's own and is the nearest we have got to adding an eighth! This means proper soft padding and support against the floor for your knees.

Secondly, there is a little trick I discovered. To create variety and to help the joint cope with any strain, I often flex the kneeling leg behind me and lift my kneeling foot off the ground. This strengthens the knee joint itself and enables me to roll onto different parts of my knee, rather than letting my weight fall through the very same part of the knee every time.

With this mastered, you have achieved the perfection of zero-strain Bodywork. A vertical back with strokes powered completely from the hips.

Look at this drawing and assess for yourself the amount of pressure needed to massage the gluteals this deeply. Can you feel the practitioner's hips providing that power from her kneeling position? Then look at her face and the utter freedom in her head and neck…

SUPPORT

Psychologically this is a tough one for most of us professional carers to get. It embraces the heretical possibility that the client is there for the practitioner! In truth the client supports the practitioner financially and in truth the practitioner develops and grows in HARA as a result of the client coming for treatment.

In my opinion, the real value of a Bodywork training is to enable us to be ever more open to the learning available from each and every client we touch.

Try this exercise:
Do this in the middle of the room – stand with your knees bent and your arms out and bent. Feel the strain. Now imagine you are suddenly transported into one of those children's ball ponds – you are in a swimming pool of little round balls....Surrounded. You no longer have to hold your arms up against gravity – they are supported by the balls. The spaces between your legs and arms and under your armpits, all are surrounded by supportive balls...Can you feel the change in strain as soon as you visualised this support?

The very same "tiring position" becomes easy and pleasurable, simply through a quantum shift in perception. Which perception is more true for you, that you are all alone, or surrounded by love and support? Which perception works best for you in your Bodywork, that you have to strain to do your work, or that you are held up by billions of molecules, each containing the energy of the Sun ?

Is it not the case that we are surrounded by millions of molecules and atoms that are holding us up, caressing us and supporting us? Does not every atom contain within it enough energy to destroy the planet? If we can but tap into the healing power of these atoms...

Now look at this drawing and see how this transfers to Bodywork. Our practitioner is leaning onto the client and the table – getting 100% support. Notice how much pleasure and joy emerges when we are properly supported.

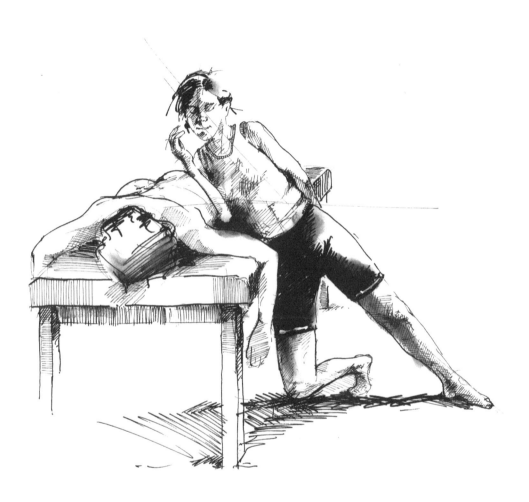

SHIRE HORSE

The SHIRE HORSE is an image that speaks volumes for the approach of NO HANDS. Using the Soft Front or the Ulna Edge or the Styloid Processes backed up by the whole of the practitioner's body – this is what SHIRE HORSE is about.

It is about the inherent strength and durability of the long bones. It is about the simple and dedicated focus of that beautiful horse ploughing the field. If 80% of Bodywork is about preparation, then it is the SHIRE HORSE who prepares the soil for planting the seeds of healing.

In addition to the actual contact surface used, the SHIRE HORSE is about the mental and physical alignment of the practitioner. Before you actually begin to apply pressure for your very next Massage stroke, just pause for a few seconds and ask yourself:

Is every part of my body aligned behind the direction of this stroke?
Is my mind clear on my purpose with this stroke?

If your intention (mental alignment) and your posture (physical alignment) are one, and if the contact surface used for your Bodywork is also strong and durable, then you have SHIRE HORSE. This is what gives your every Bodywork movement, no matter how large or small, true potency.

Look at this drawing – I asked John to remove the client. NO HANDS is almost exclusively about practitioner self-awareness. Notice the power of such alignment – in particular look at the back heel against the ground. Now look at the relaxed expression John captured in my face…

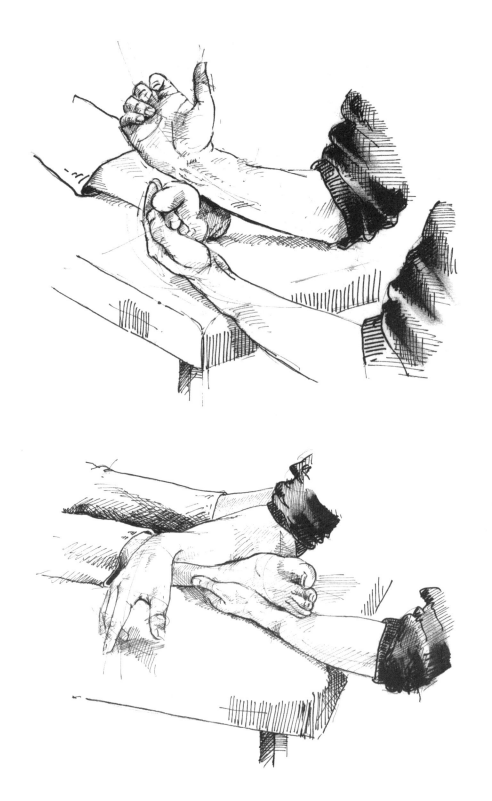

WORKING THE REFLEXES

What follows in the next section are seven different positions from which I give some of my bodywork. Like any good book, the best and most important bit is in the pictures and in all the spaces....

Reading about this is a bit like giving a NO HANDS session – you need to take your time to breathe and enjoy these amazing drawings… allow your whole body to feel as you breathe and look.

Become lost in the bodywork of these drawings – they speak volumes

OPENING THE GATEWAY

I picture this important Mind-Body gateway as a circle or sphincter muscle at the base of the skull. It is a gateway that gets rusty and needs repeated 'oiling'. I believe that this is an energetic centre that needs to be opened every time I give bodywork. I press slowly and deeply into these tissues, compressing and then releasing…

So I slow down, take time to focus on my breath, Grow my HARA….

Then I give more slow traction, so I can see the heels of her feet moving. I remember this single truth:

Masterful bodywork is sensitive bodywork
Sensitive bodywork is slow bodywork
Therefore Masterful bodywork is slow bodywork

Slow, thoughtful, powerful movements. Breathing deeply, taking my time. Giving her tissues time to go with this pressure. Working one part of her body in this profound way, enables her to release tension throughout her whole body. A full therapeutic treatment before I even begin to think of her feet reflexes…

Look into the space between her head and my chest, because that is where its all happening….in the space

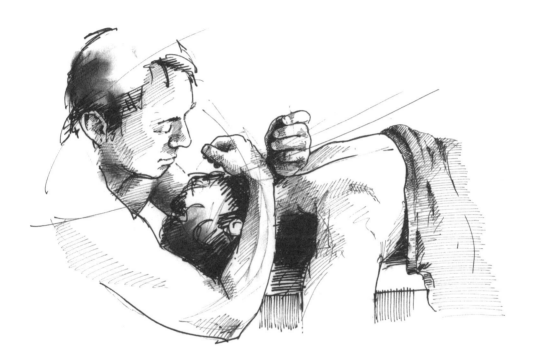

EARTHING THE CLIENT

This practitioner sits comfortably on her own leg......Securing the client's ankle against her own body she rocks her HARA backwards....and stretches the client's whole body. The way she does this invites a deep letting go of both physical and mental tension throughout the client's body.

It is the practitioner's belly that pulls this client towards her feet, not her hands. Done correctly, this movement is achieved with hardly any muscle strength at all – it is done entirely from the HARA.

She draws the client's energy and awareness down the body, along with her bodyweight, right down into her feet.

So now, the client's mind is connected with her feet ...this is the sort of Earthing that can cure a headache instantly...

Can you feel the practitioner's stillness, her poise? Can you feel the amount of energy emanating from her belly, the HARA?

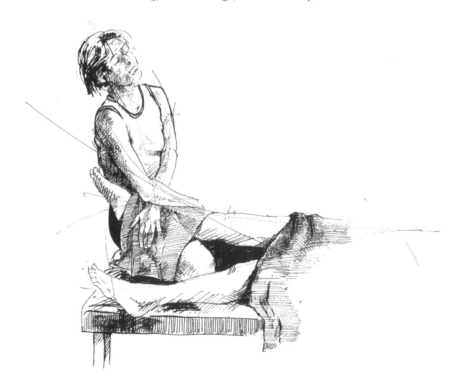

Another really powerful way to Earth the client into her body almost instantly is by using my Soft Front to press my client's shoulders away from her head, as in the drawing below. Done slowly and deeply, this position not only opens up her body-mind connection but also releases any tension the shoulder-neck girdle.

Encouraging my client to 'let go' - both physically and mentally. Helping her to enter into that trance-like and meditative state which deepens the impact and power of all bodywork treatments.

SOFTENING THE SOIL

Using oil, and from a comfortable kneeling position, I soften and loosen all her leg muscles. Like rain on hard and dry Earth…

Soft wrists. Soft Front. Gentle mulching, slow and deep. With everything loose I can still create a bow wave of her muscles in front of my arm…

Feel the depth and the slow softness within this drawing…

I use my hand as a guide along the side of her leg, for roundedness and psychological completion. I keep my back vertical in this kneeling position and power all my movement from the hips – I could do this all day.

Alternatively without using any oil, I can also gently compress and release her leg muscles through clothing until all the cows have come home from all of their fields…

A hundred different strokes pour out from such a position…

This drawing shows me completing all this leg work by warming and opening up the muscles of the foot in preparation for the next stage.

Sense the thoughtful depth and power of this position…

The fact that I could do this stroke forever lends power to my movements. Any tension in my client's foot stands helpless before the power available to me from my whole bodyweight….and I choose to go softly…infusing the moment with both power and magic….

My hips circle backwards as if going under the table. I sink my weight into the client's foot…immersing myself in the stories of this foot, lost entirely in the moment…

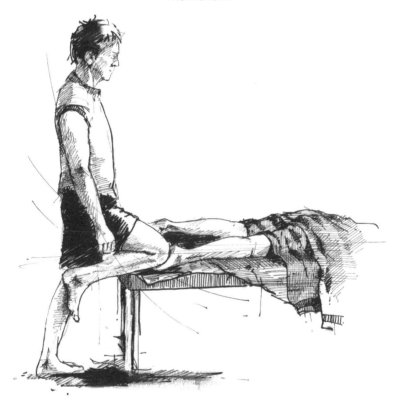

The aim of this stage is to further open and soften the client's muscle tissue. This is done by relaxing the client's legs and opening up all the channels of energy between the foot and the torso, enhancing the effectiveness of any reflex stimulation that follows…

THE MANGLE

I squash her feet between the softness of my forearms, squashing out the air…

From this comfortable kneeling position I can use my whole bodyweight and the strength of my shoulders to work deeply into all the muscles of her foot. Powerful pressing and squashing movements…stretching movements…The value of stretching the foot in this way is massive for releasing reflexes throughout her foot.

My wrists remain loose and floppy and inside I am smiling at the effortlessness of it all…

Different angles of leaning and movement produce release in her whole leg and body. Notice the VERTICALITY of my posture. My shoulders provide the stability and strength to clamp the foot securely so that any of my body movements create the massage.

Look closely and allow yourself to feel the contentment in this movement – the almost smug pleasure of such zero-strain bodywork…

All three drawings, whether prone or supine, capture the 'Mangling' effect possible with the wondrous Soft Front. Such deep pressure from the practitioner…yet my client's face almost always registers sheer pleasure… the joy and the ecstasy of tension release in her foot – and consequently her whole body…

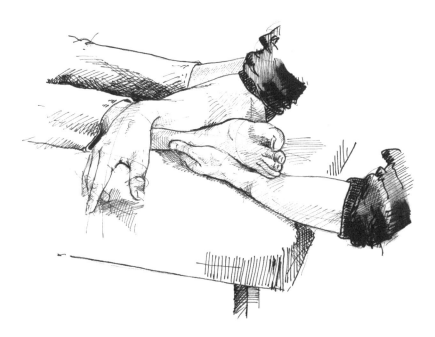

Opening up the musculature of the foot. Releasing all the muscles, tendons, ligaments and bones of the foot. Revealing the reflexes hiding underneath. Like whales, they rise gently from the depths to the surface for air…

Thus released, the reflexes begin to 'fire'….
They do not know that the Reflexology treatment hasn't begun yet!

A THOUGHT...

The next stage is all about stimulating specific reflex points. We will travel there together – but let us just stop here a moment…

Let us pause a little in our bodywork and focus on our clients…

Let us empty our heads of all our therapeutic treatment plans and goals…

Let us contemplate a new possibility:

Maybe just blowing on these reflexes or singing to them will do the trick now…

Maybe the bodywork is so complete that the client's own healing can take over…

Maybe the cataclysmic healing forces within each molecule have already been unleashed by our work…

It is important that we listen to the wisdom inside the depths of our HARA and ask ourselves these two questions:

How much more Bodywork is needed?
How much has already been accomplished?

All our clients really care about are the gentle susurrations of healing now humming and murmuring throughout their bodies.

And if we do decide to go further, or we have this irresistible urge to shout "I just have to use my fingers or thumbs!", then our clients already have feet that are so open and soft that *the slightest pressure may be all we need…*

LEVERS

Supporting the client's foot with my non-working hand I am using the styloid process of my ulna edge to stimulate her spinal reflexes.

Can you feel the restraint and 'held back' power of this focused work?

This is a classic zero – strain position as I am totally comfortable and supported. I could stay here for hours, except that my client would be begging me to stop. This is at the heart of all NO HANDS – to be able to continue well beyond the tolerance of my clients!

Notice the support that I am giving myself by leaning my arms against the plinth. It is the Postural Secret of SUPPORT that fills my mind during this work. Using my elbow as a pivot against the plinth I can use leverage to apply pressure…

Feel the slowness of my work and the attention to my own body movements…

From such a relaxed and powerful position, I can attend to the minutia of my client's feet and seek out any reflexes that I wish...

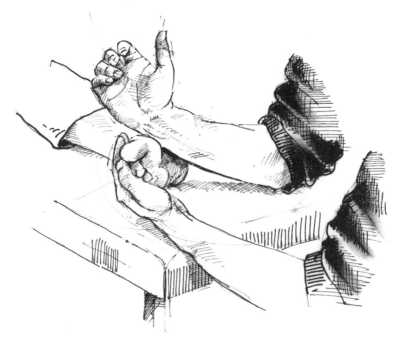

DRILLING

Let me say this right away:

The truth of the matter is that I can feel as much through my elbows, arms and whole body movements as I can through my fingers and thumbs.

Nobody believes me at first, but those practitioners who persist discover this to be true, the same way as you discover the incredible sensitivity of your palms after you begin the practice of Bodywork.

In this drawing you can see me sinking into the very deepest layers of the foot. Yet there is such gentleness and such control…Notice the supporting hand under my client's ankle.

Sometimes I use this position to open up even more musculature, sometimes to stimulate the reflex points...

PRECISION

The irony of NO HANDS is that we often use the fingers and hands – but without any possibility of injury. Sometimes we just have to feel those gritty little nodules of crystalline deposits disintegrating under our fingers and thumbs!

For this, the position you can see in this drawing is ideal. All the work is done through my elbow, pressing into the top of my thumb. So the thumb becomes a passive pad from which to feel the tissues. There is no muscular tension anywhere in my left hand and fingers. It is 100% passive and relaxed.

See how the line of dynamic loading runs from my left leg across to my right shoulder and down my right arm. I am concentrating on FALLING into my thumb and my client's foot. Again, there are many different angles to work from in this position.

This supported thumb work can be used anywhere on the foot…

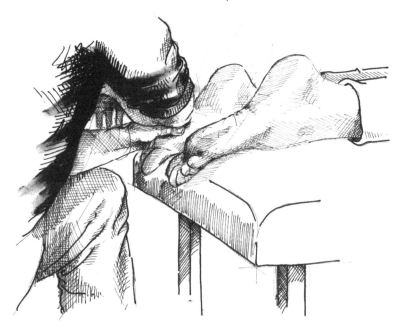

The lightest of touch can now stimulate my client's reflexes. Within each of these positions there is also potential for great power and precision. The exact pressure that you need in order to effectively stimulate the reflexes can be heard deep inside the caverns of your HARA…

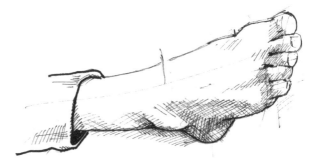

THE BIG PICTURE

Let us talk about the desert for a moment

The desert of touch.

When you let a drop of water fall upon the hardy desert flower
(Just one drop mind)
It springs up like a whirling dervish
To give an outrageous display of vitality, colour and life energy.
And do you really think that flower concerns itself
With where the water comes from?

For years it has been sitting quietly,
Awaiting its moment to dance
And when that tiny drop of water flows into its veins
It springs up with such pent up beauty,
Incandescent in the dawn
To dance a song about life itself!

Do you really think the flower cares whether the water
Came from this or that particular cloud?

We therapists need to be careful
As we argue the merits of this or that particular brand of therapy

Because we are talking about TOUCH.

Touch in the desert,
Touch to the harmed and touch to the bereft.

We are talking about people who have sat in the desert for YEARS
Waiting for someone to touch their parched tissues.

To simply say:
"I am here. Rest easy. Breathe,
Drink deeply of this touch
And let us see what is possible

So that, God willing,
Some divine reconfiguration can be achieved
In this moment that we share together."

So let us not waste our precious time
arguing about the benefits of this or that therapy.

Let us get out there and pour the healing waters of touch
Upon the desert flower that is humanity.

Let us always see

THE BIG PICTURE

A PERSONAL NOTE

Using your forearms instead of hands sounds simple enough, doesn't it?

Or does it?

The purpose of this trilogy of books is to show you just what a myth that statement is. Know this simple truth:

If you start to use your forearms for more than a few seconds at a time without the proper training in such a paradigm shift you will hurt your clients and yourself much more than if you carried on using your hands.

My injuries and the solutions I found over the first 5 years, only qualified me to say it worked for me. That was about my own clinical and professional survival. The 10 years I then spent with over 20 practitioners and their clients in over a quarter of a million sessions qualified me to say it works for the profession. In order that I could sleep at night I needed to be sure this approach worked absolutely. It is these fifteen years of persistent clinical testing that qualify me to state that:

Learning how to adapt your existing knowledge of Bodywork to the use of forearms and other body parts requires a complete rethink of your body movements - if you are to avoid additional injury.

The dangers in learning this approach without proper guidance can be fully understood by the following:

In the first years, teaching FALLING to practitioners gave us all back ache! We were straining our backs to lean over our clients…It took over three years to identify the problem, identify the cause of it and evolve the three-step system of FALLING. Now we fall with zero-strain.

Only after all these years did I begin to show my approach to a profession I respect too deeply to suggest changes without good reason.

In general, the profession should be very wary of self-styled 'experts' who suggest that you "Just use your forearms a bit more" to avoid injury. These are the same people who were laughing at me 15 years ago when I began to suggest there was an injury problem for our profession.

Now, because of my work in this field, it has become accepted that Swedish Massage techniques are causing injury. As Gandhi said "First they ignore you, then they mock you and finally they listen to you". Nowadays, I would also add to Gandhi's words "And then they try to copy you". Many trainers are now jumping onto this injury bandwagon for financial gain without the proper study or clinical experience. Ask these people what they were doing fifteen years ago!

So for your own protection, make sure that you only learn how to adapt your Bodywork to using other parts of your body from someone who has done the learning necessary. At going to press, I know of no practitioners other than my registered trainers who have done sufficient or due diligence to this important subject. I do not want to restrict anyone's learning – I only want to make it safe.

EPILOGUE TO A TRILOGY

This book is a completion. It is with some emotion that I come to the end of this trilogy. If someone had said that I had to re-examine all of the basic principles to Bodywork, so that touch could continue to spread across the Globe in the 21st Century without any fear of injury to its valued exponents, I would have replied "Impossible!".

Luckily, in 1989, no one told me this, so I just went from one logical step to the next…

> 15 years later, two wrist injuries, a quarter of a million NO HANDS Massages, 7 trainers, 3 books, 20 articles, 7 courses, 1 smash hit performance massage, 50 seminars and 7 training manuals later I can honestly say:
> "My NO HANDS work is done".

Apart from the continuing job of alerting our profession to the dangers of injury and the new zero-strain technology now available through my work, of course!

So, if you have travelled through all three books with me, I would like to personally thank you for reading this and coming so far with me. Without the open-mindedness of practitioners like you, I could not have got beyond even the first year. It has been an honour and a privilege to get to know you.

To meet and work beside so many gifted practitioners of touch has been a daily joy for me. If we have not met personally, then it is my sincere hope that we will do so in the future.

Nor should you mistake this epilogue for an epitaph! The next stage of my work is equally exciting…

You see, this trilogy has all been about Shi'Zen (balance)

Reclaiming the ancient balance in healing, where the practitioner is not hurt and both client and practitioner benefit from the exchange.

Just as ancient civilisations knew the importance of connection with the earth, so they knew the healing power of touch and gave and received freely to each other on a daily basis. Nowadays we have separated this into the role of the giver and receiver. Therapist and client. Money changes hands to attempt to put right this imbalance. It does not. Injury happens. NO HANDS is about putting that ancient Shi'Zen back into Bodywork. Re-forging that ancient synergy of healing...So practitioners can stay in Bodywork long enough to become true masters of touch, without needing to retire from injury or exhaustion.

NO HANDS is just the first of three layers for reclaiming the Shi'Zen of Bodywork. Ancient healers used 'the word'. The second layer is all about the amazing power of language and music when combined with powerful touch. Some of the latest technologies of the mind, communication and psychotherapy are now reaching back to learn and harness the ancients' wisdom in their use of the word in healing.

And the third layer? Well, if you can keep a secret then lean a little closer and read this very quietly..... it is about the Shi'Zen to be found through energy manipulation. It is, in truth, nothing less than the training of real life Bodywork wizards!

So watch this space!

NOTES

I use this section of the book to reference wherever possible, the deliberate closeness of the approach of NO HANDS to the original writings of Reflexology's founder, Eunice Ingham. Whilst the actual physical work may look somewhat different to the onlooker, the philosophical roots of her approach are truly honoured by this author.

I therefore offer quotations only from that great lady's books – hence only page numbers are given as references. Her models or maps of the healing body were sufficient to transform the world of healing and affect the health of thousands – possibly millions. In this sense the truth of her explanations is less important to me than their potency. She wrote:

Don't let the common mistake of its simplicity rob it of any importance. The why and wherefore I am not prepared to explain. I only ask that you try it out. (1/2)

figures in brackets refer to pages in two books by Eunice Ingham:
book one: *Stories the feet can tell thru Reflexology*
book two: *Stories the feet have told thru Reflexology*
1/6 refers to page six in book one; 2/6 refers to page six in book two.

SECTION I: BACKGROUND

THE SEVEN STAGES OF INJURY AND REFLEXOLOGY

There is a discussion on this topic in the appendix.

NO HANDS

For Eunice Ingham, Reflexology was a simple matter of stimulating the tender spots on the feet. *It is neither hard nor difficult and will only require a little study and practice to make you as proficient as anyone in determining the location to be manipulated for any ailment. (I/7)*

Nor was she averse to the odd little simple ditty:

> *"If you're feeling out of kilter*
> *Don't know why or what about*
> *Let your feet reveal the answer*
> *Find the sore spot work it out"*
>   Eunice D Ingham

She distanced herself from the common practice in Zone Therapy of using implements, preferring the human contact of hands. Providing the tender spots can be massaged adequately and sensitively, I do not believe there is a conflict in using other parts of the practitioner's body to achieve this. Knowing that there is a safe alternative for therapists would, I believe, have interested Eunice Ingham enormously. As it is, she wrote and worked in a time when the issue of Injury had not yet developed for the profession.

The logic of my 4-stage treatment protocol is about creating a whole body flow and an increase in circulation – something that should enhance the effects of Reflexology. Eunice Ingham herself saw circulation at the very heart of all healing:
We must remember, circulation is life; stagnation is death (I/94)

Keep in mind first and uppermost what you are doing. You are stimulating the circulation, and as you stimulate the circulation you raise the body vitality, and as the vitality increases, nature has the strength to overcome and throw off the poisons in the system. (I/8)

Ingham made the map of how reflexology works very clear in her writings. Our circulation can become sluggish at the extremities for a number of reasons. Crystalline deposits form which need breaking up or they affect the functioning of our organs.

You can readily see how necessary it is that we keep the chemical balance of our blood stream normal and free from crystalline deposits so the feet will have no serious stories to tell. (I/1)

Our body is said to be sixty percent fluid. How necessary it is to have this flowing through the tissue in a healthy condition and not overburdened with poisonous acid. (1/4)

...normal nerve force depends on normal circulation(2/42)

The importance of opening up, loosening and realigning the whole foot is covered in many places in her writing. Such manipulations have a value all of their own in their circulatory effects and general rebalancing. When writing about general foot massage and twisting she says:

If any one or more of the 26 bones of the foot should be misplaced, nature fills in that misplaced joint with a calcium deposit which we can help to loosen and dissolve by this form of Reflexology.....You will readily see how this will help nature to carry away any such foreign matter which interferes with the normal position of the bones. (1/74)

According to Eunice Ingham, such deposits would in turn, hinder the proper functioning of the reflex organ to that point.

With regard to my working all foot reflexes, this approach developed from the homeostatic teachings of Eunice Ingham herself. Contrary to a lot of modern Reflexology teaching she never saw a danger in working a lot of reflexes:

Since it is certain no harm can be done by working on a reflex, there is no need to hesitate, but set out to do all the good that can be accomplished. (1/47)

At no point in her writing does she suggest that pressing a reflex could cause damage. She only warns against over stimulation because of the effects of too much detoxification on the client. Nothing bad is going on when a client detoxifies rapidly – it is just a little unpleasant in the short term.

If the reaction is severe, do not give another treatment too soon. Let a few days elapse to give nature a chance to adjust itself to the increased circulation. (1/53)

The profound effects that relaxation and encouraging general systemic circulation can have on the body are emphasised throughout Eunice Ingham's writings. With the new approach of NO HANDS it is now possible to work all the reflexes of the foot in just a matter of minutes – prior to any specific working of sore points. Each therapist must of course decide for herself just what Reflex stimulation she is comfortable with.

THE HISTORICAL REFLEX

Eunice Ingham's genealogy can be found in her preface. Additional biographical details and genealogy can be found in the appendix "About Eunice Ingham". So much of Eunice Ingham's approach is based on the solid naturopathic principles of circulation and elimination:

The old method of soaking the feet in hot mustard water, taking a sweat bath, etc., all had its effect in relaxing and opening the pores of the body, helping nature in its process of elimination (1/28)

When writing about stimulating the colon reflex:

Increased circulation can become a powerful housecleaning agent, and thus stimulate a rectal action in a normal regular rhythm without the use of drugs (1/77)

So much illness can come down to the simplest of causes such as unhappiness or lack of sleep or lack of basic exercise:

Our body is constructed to endure a lot of abuse. We have been breaking the laws of nature over a period of months and years, and it will take time to rebuild and replace these sick broken down cells(1/93)

Many of us privileged to work in clinical practice for over 20 years discover that most clients pay very little attention to their maintenance, only coming to us when things have got very bad:

We are inclined to give the working of our automobile more thought and consideration than we do our precious body (1/93)

Our plug into Gaia is explained with the electrical analogy:

The nerves of our body may be likened to an electrical system. It will be our ability to make the normal contact with the electricity in the ground, through our feet and from the elements or atmosphere surrounding us, that will determine the degree of power we are able to manifest ……. Trying to get a normal contact where there is congestion in these nerve terminals in the feet is like trying to put a plug into a defective fixture.(2/2)

She also uses the electrical analogy of terminals to reinforce her map of congestion in the reflexes:

Now if these terminals are corroded, if we may use that term, through the lack of normal force supplied from the heart action, over a period of the past, we will improve that vital contact with the electrical forces of the Earth obtained under normal conditions, if we can eliminate any foreign substance from the delicate nerve areas. (2/67)

THE POLITICAL REFLEX

Whilst this is an obvious point to make, so much of modern Reflexology wants to be seen as a quasi-medical activity. Eunice Ingham herself was quite clear about this point:

…you are only applying a particular form of compression technique to the reflexes of the feet. You are not diagnosing. You are not prescribing. You are in no way practicing medicine, but simply using a reflex method to help relieve nerve tension to stimulate the circulation so nature can restore the normal functioning of the various glands and organs of the body. (2/35)

Taking off our shoes may seem a little thing, but the life force we thereby make available to ourselves through the Earth and the stimulation of the nerve endings in our feet is staggering.

Eunice Ingham had a lot to say about this imprisonment of the foot inside the shoe:

Our feet we carefully preserve in a shoe, which prevents a certain amount of the natural motion of the foot that would take place if we were constantly walking barefoot in the primitive way nature intended us to follow...nature intended that we should walk, bend, twist our feet and also run occasionally to keep a fresh supply of blood, with the normal circulation surging through every minute joint and nerve extremity of our feet. (1/10)

That there was nothing natural about the shoe is another simplistic observation. This barrier between our feet and the Earth has had its destructive effect upon our instinctive connection with nature and with all that is natural. The themes of what is natural and what healing nature can work on us can be seen throughout Eunice Ingham's writings:

Don't try to improve on God's natural laws of nature. It is only as we abuse these precious laws that we suffer from the many ills mankind has fallen heir to. (1/78) (see appendix 7 "about shoes")

This fixation on the power of all that is natural is in line with Eunice Ingham's strong belief in the naturopathic principles of circulation and elimination. The importance of stimulation was synonymous with exercise – exercise that is severely limited by the shoe. She writes:

Reflexology in any form is only a means of exercise, a means of equalising the circulation. Everything around us that is alive is in motion. (1/104)

Sometimes the most powerful therapeutic interventions are the simplest. You need to rest so your body can rebuild itself and fight off illness. You need a healthy diet. You need fresh air and exercise. You need lots of water so your body can eliminate toxins. You need good and regular bowel movements to release the waste matter from your cellular tissue. These are the tenets of the naturopathic approach to healing. You can almost hear the exasperation in her voice (and perhaps the stamping of her foot!) after a lifetime of saying such things to her clients when she talks about taking care of the feet:

If people would only realise the importance of taking better care of their feet, we would have less sickness in our land today. (2/66)

THE MUSCULAR REFLEX

This issue of really opening up the foot is at the heart of NO HANDS. Deep muscular massage of the foot and realignment of the bones have a powerful reflex effect on the whole body. Eunice Ingham's own writing makes it clear just how important both the structural and muscular health of the foot is:

Thus we can see the benefit of any form of therapy or exercise that might increase the circulation and strengthen the action of our muscles. (1/1)

In this quotation she places the origin of much illness in the breakdown of the foot's structure:

...the muscle tissue in our feet gives way. The body structure goes down and one or more of the twenty six bones in each foot may become misplaced causing undue pressure on some nerve ending. This shuts off a certain portion of the normal nerve and blood supply in the bottom of the feet, and as any part of the blood stream becomes choked, it slows down the circulation. As a result of this slowing down of the circulation we have a formation of chemical deposits or waste matter forming in and around the misplaced joints....If this obstruction happens to be in the nerve endings or reflex leading to the kidneys, we find the kidneys are being robbed of a part of their blood supply. This in turn interferes with the proper contraction and relaxation that is necessary in order that the kidneys may carry out their part of eliminating the uric acid from the system.(1/3)

If the muscles of the foot are tense or firm, then the work of the Reflexologist is obviously made harder:

I find more often with those where the muscles are firm, it requires considerable pressure to find the reflexes. (1/61)

In one of her photos she shows her fist working and loosening the musculature of the foot, and in another it shows her manipulating all the bones of the foot with a twisting and rotating movement (2/32). The stage 3 work of NO HANDS is but a logical development of this. There is no doubt that this powerful foot massage can produce deep release of tension throughout the client's body and mind. It can powerfully pump the system of the body and stimulate circulation – especially when the practitioner can use whole bodyweight.

Eunice Ingham often refers to the importance of circulation and flow and in one excerpt likens the work of the Reflexologist to that of the plumber:

This poison or debris in the blood stream may be likened to a plumbing system where the drain pipes require the attention of a plumber. He takes the rubber cup with a handle...and starts pulsating, creating a terrific intermittent pressure, freeing the drain of all obstructions....(with Reflexology, we can) create a renewed amount of circulation by setting up a pulsating system which loosens any crystalline formation of residue from the blood stream, putting it into suspension where eventually it can be eliminated.(2/42)

THE ALPHA STATE

Today, the need to have mentally soothing treatments as well as physically effective ones is even more pronounced than in Eunice Ingham's day. She was possibly one of the first writers to describe the integral effect of mood and emotion upon the body's organs.

Her descriptions of the mind-body link were way ahead of her time and she should be recognized for this just as much as for her Reflexology writing. In particular she regarded the seven major glands in the body as being the link between our thoughts and feelings and our bodily health:

Remember every thought and emotion affects our glands and every thought is either constructive or destructive. Our glands are health builders, each pouring out secretions, which if in harmony, health is the result. If any one of the seven principle glands of the body fail to function, our whole mechanism is out of order. *(1/29)*

She also followed the classic approach of naturopathy by emphasising over and over again the importance of healthy elimination:

It is allotted to our skin to throw off and send out three pints of poison a day. It is said that if this were to be injected back into the blood stream we would die in three days of blood poisoning.(1/42)

She then goes on to make the connection between tension in the mind and the physical closure of our pores:

Now, suppose we are all tightened up and worrying over something that tenses and tightens all the pores of the body so that we fail to throw off this allotted portion of poison. (1/42)

Tension in the body is an integral part of the disease picture. If we can relax the client's whole body and mind in each treatment then we are honouring this basic principle of healing.

There is not an organ in the body that is not affected by the mind. Every thought we think either has a constructive or a destructive reaction on the chemical content of our blood stream.....the twenty seven trillion cells of the body all have their thinking machine, and they all respond to the law of suggestion. It is the law of creation and we cannot tamper with it. (1/98)

It is an acknowledged fact that the body is affected by the mind. Every flitting change of the mind causes a chemical change in the body. Circulation follows attention. We are told that the centre of every cell in the body is composed of the same grey matter as the brain. (1/99)

The 4-stage protocol allows for the client to settle fully into the calm and soothing alpha brain wave pattern where the parasympathetic nervous system kicks in and the natural rebalancing mechanisms of the body are activated. It is no good pressing the feet whilst the client is tense, and as bodyworkers we can employ the knowledge of centuries to help the client relax. The systemic power of the new appraoch of NO HANDS makes this both rapid and effortless.

...if one is full of fear and worry he becomes tense and unable to relax. The circulation becomes partially choked in certain areas, the tiny capillaries in the feet become choked with a crystalline deposit formation, interfering with the circulation...(2/30)

SECTION 2: SEVEN POSTURAL SECRETS

More writing on this subject can be found in the first two volumes of this trilogy. In this book I wanted the drawings of John Coombes to do the talking. Because of the nature of Reflexology, I have used whole body drawings from Massage to illustrate the Postural Secrets. This is so that you can see the effect of the Postural Secret 'writ large' throughout the Bodyworkers whole body. Much of our NO HANDS Reflex training course involves translating this into the smaller movements needed for the feet.

SECTION 3: WORKING THE REFLEXES

Again, the drawings are an integral part of this section. These drawings communicate so much more about NO HANDS than any amount of words. Regarding the issue of not seeing the client's facial expression, I am aware that this breaks with Eunice Ingham's tradition. However, many of the principles of working the reflexes with NO HANDS can be adapted from the supine positions for use with the client sitting. Once clients have experienced it lying down they often choose this over sitting. We have developed a very simple and accurate finger signal system of communication for the prone client, so they can convey any measure of discomfort immediately. Each Reflexologist will have her own philosophy to follow regarding working with or through pain and this book is not telling Reflexologists how to treat their clients.

APPENDIX 1: EUNICE INGHAM'S GEANEALOGY

The Bodywork origins of Reflexology reach back to many ancient cultures. Different forms of working the feet have been used all over the ancient world. Images of feet being massaged are found in most ancient cultures. The physician's tomb at Saqqara is one famous example. This form of healing through the feet may well have spread from Egypt via the Roman Empire.

Zone Theory was the modern precursor to Reflexology. This began with the work of Dr. William H. Fitzgerald. He was an Ear, Nose and Throat specialist working at the Boston City Hospital, as well as in hospitals in Connecticut and London. He called his work Zone Analgesia. Fitzgerald applied pressure to the corresponding bony eminence or to the zones corresponding to the location of the injury and made use of elastic bands, clothes pegs and aluminium combs on the hands, surgical clamps for the tongue, nasal probes and a retractor for the pharynx. Fitzgerald was responsible for formulating the first chart on the longitudinal zones of the body. He also discovered that the application of pressure on the zones not only relieved pain but in some cases, also relieved the underlying cause as well. Reflexology is based on this discovery.

Dr. Shelby Riley, M.D. worked closely with Dr. Fitzgerald and developed the Zone Theory further. He added horizontal zones across the hands and feet, together with the longitudinal zones and determined individual reflexes. Riley is the link between Zone Theory and Eunice Ingham. She worked closely with Dr. Riley and was fascinated by the concept of Zone Therapy and started developing her foot reflex theory in the early 1930's.

With Riley, Eunice Ingham had the opportunity to treat hundreds of patients where each reflex point of contact had been carefully and thoughtfully checked and rechecked until she was able to determine that the reflexes on the feet were an exact mirror image of the organs of the body. Dr. Riley encouraged her to write her first book entitled "Stories The Feet Can Tell" where she documented her cases and carefully mapped out the reflexes on the feet as we know them today. This book was published in 1938 and was later translated into seven different languages which spread the benefits of Reflexology worldwide.

After the publication of her book Eunice Ingham travelled around the country giving book reviews. Many sick people attended these book reviews/workshops where she would teach people by working on them and discuss their particular health problems. As these sick people got better, the word spread and Reflexology became better known amongst both medics and lay people.

In the late 50's Dwight Byers started helping Eunice Ingham at her workshops. In 1961 Dwight Byers and his sister Eusebia Messenger, joined their Aunt Eunice teaching at workshops on a full time basis. Seven years later they became responsible for the continued teaching of Reflexology under the banner of The National Institute of Reflexology. Eunice died in 1974 at the age of 85 still thoroughly convinced that Reflexology could aid in easing the suffering of mankind. She was on the road with this simple message until the age of 80.

By which time, Reflexology was established throughout the world.

APPENDIX 2: EUNICE INGHAM'S MIND MAP

Much is made of her wonderful maps of the feet with the organs superimposed upon them. A great deal less is made of the map Eunice Ingham obviously carried in her head regarding the whys and wherefores of her work and the reason for the effectiveness of Reflex stimulation.

Here are some of my own observations regarding the imagery she uses throughout her writings. I believe that the map we hold in our mind can massively contribute to or destroy our Bodywork.

To understand this fully, try giving a halfway decent Bodywork session to a client whilst repeating the following sentence to yourself: "All Bodywork is just a waste of time and money". How does this compare with the Bodywork you give when repeating the following ancient Jewish dictum: "If you help just one person, you help the whole world"?

This demonstrates the importance of the images we hold in our minds. For this reason the images inside the mind of Eunice Ingham as suggested by her writings are a worthy subject for study.

BLOOD
It is clear that the state of the blood made a real difference to Eunice Ingham. This is in line with the naturopathic approaches of the osteopathic and chiropractic communities of the day to disease. She took it one step further and saw acidity in the blood as contaminating the efficient functioning of the foot reflexes. To her, the formation of crystalline deposits at the nerve endings in the feet would inhibit and make sluggish the activities of their reflex organs:

But if we allow an excess acid condition to form in our blood stream, we increase the calcium deposits. Then acid crystals similar to particles of frost when examined under microscope, form in these nerve endings, thus impeding the normal circulation of the blood to the various parts of the body. (1/10)

NERVES
This congestion at the ends of the feet will in turn inhibit the nerve function and supply to that organ. This duality of blood circulation and nerve action seem very closely linked in Eunice Ingham's mind. Both nerve function and circulation were improved through reflex stimulation:

The point where the greatest amount of tenderness is found will determine the location of the greatest amount of congestion, and where congestion exists disease will result. (1/13)

NATUROPATHY
The importance of exercise, tone and the proper muscular functioning of the whole body and the foot can be found throughout her writings. For example, whilst writing about the kidney reflexes in the feet she states:

If the muscular action becomes insufficient to keep the nerve endings free from all crystalline deposits, these important organs of elimination will fail to function properly (1/58)

STRUCTURAL INTEGRITY

Proper structural alignment was a major part of her approach – pure osteopathy in fact!

A misplaced vertebra, in any part of the spine, will be sure to cut off the normal circulation and interfere with the contracting and relaxing of the part which is depending upon this particular nerve for its blood supply…. Remember every part of our body receives its nerve supply from some part of the spine, and a big majority of our ailments today can be traced to some misplacement or impinged nerve tightening the muscles of some part holding it that way with this abnormal tension. (1/56)

The role of working the foot is clear – the Chinese dictum "as above, so below" would apply here. To release congestion and misalignment of the spinal foot will release congestion and misalignment in the spine:

…we find the corresponding location in the spinal reflexes very tender; but by applying plenty of this reflexology method…we will be sure to help nature repair whatever may have gone haywire. (1/4)

It seems clear to me that Eunice Ingham was able to help thousands of people to better health through holding such a specific mind map inside her head – whatever its medical or scientific veracity.

This author sees the following image permeating throughout all of Eunice Ingham's writings:

Each organ in the body can be regarded as a mini heart pump, sending blood to the feet, where circulation becomes slower because of the capillaries close to the reflex point. The blood then returns to the organ directly. If the circulation becomes too sluggish at the capillary exchange in the foot reflex, then crystalline deposits occur. This can happen for several reasons – poor organ strength, rather like a weak heart, unable to pump the blood powerfully to the extremities or poor foot health causing obstructions and congestions to occur. Whatever the reason, if the blood is sluggish in returning to this organ, then its vitality and proper functioning is further reduced.

Parallel to this blood circulation is nerve circulation. We must imagine a nerve running directly from the organ into the corresponding reflex point in the foot, and back again. Stimulation of this nerve end provides healthy stimulation to the organ – keeping it vital and healthy. Lack of exercise or congestion through crystalline deposits can reduce this nerve activity, causing the organ to reduce in efficient functioning. Likewise, a poorly functioning organ will produce a congested and painful nerve ending.

Any congestion or nerve impairment or poor organ functioning results in tenderness at the reflex:

The point where the greatest amount of tenderness is found will determine the location of the greatest amount of congestion, and where congestion exists disease will result. (1/13)

This image pours out of her writings – I myself read and re-read her work many times and found not one conflict of language to this image throughout the whole of her writing. If these are the images and maps that helped her to do the amazing work she did, then that will do for me. Whatever the veracity of this image, Eunice Ingham was very clear about what mattered most to her – helping people.

Don't let the common mistake of its simplicity rob it of any importance. (1/2)

If it was to be a contest between theoretical scientific exactitude or the empiricism of actual healing results I am certain that Eunice Ingham would have chosen the latter. She is reported to have said:

Whether my theory is right or wrong, I am getting results.

What is most interesting about this mind map is its similarity to the Chinese and Indian systems of medicine. Here, the health of internal organs is assessed by taking different aspects of the pulse in the wrist. Although it is the heart that is being felt through the pulse, different organs are perceived at different pressures and locations on that pulse. It is as if each organ truly does have its own heart pump! The whole foundation of Acupuncture and Chinese medicine is based upon the reflex effect that stimulation in one part of the body can have on other organs.

Keeping the simple image of pressing a certain part of the foot to enhance both blood and nerve stimulation to its reflexive part in the body is a powerful focus of intention and activity. Such focus will invariably produce healing results, and may well represent an energetic truth far deeper than mere anatomy and physiology can provide us with at this time.

It may be truly said that if the feet are kept in perfect health, no organ in the body can be unhealthy. If one will be sure to keep his feet in an entire state of health, he may be certain that he cannot be sick in any department of his systems. (1/3)

I think Eunice Ingham's mind map of the body is most clearly seen in this particular extract:

...the muscle tissue in our feet gives way. The body structure goes down and one or more of the twenty six bones in each foot may become misplaced causing undue pressure on some nerve ending. This shuts off a certain portion of the normal nerve and blood supply in the bottom of the feet, and as any part of the blood stream becomes choked, it slows down the circulation. As a result of this slowing down of the circulation we have a formation of chemical deposits or waste matter forming in and around the misplaced joints....If this obstruction happens to be in the nerve endings or reflex leading to the kidneys, we find the kidneys are being robbed of a part of their blood supply. This in turn interferes with the proper contraction and relaxation that is necessary in order that the kidneys may carry out their part of eliminating the uric acid from the system.(1/3)

APPENDIX 3: THE EXTENT OF INJURY

We are experiencing an injury pandemic that is crippling the Bodywork profession, and no one seems to be noticing...

As far as I know the only study into the health of practitioners anywhere in the world was commissioned by myself from a company experienced in carrying out studies across different industries (Watson, 2000).

The results indicated that 78% of Massage therapists had experienced injury to their wrists or hands. Many who filled in the questionnaire had either left the profession because of this or had reduced their workload to a pitiful financial level.

Travelling around the UK I get to talk to audiences of several hundred Bodywork therapists at a time – so I have seen, met and talked with thousands of practitioners. At these seminars I always ask for a show of hands for people who are at each of the different stages of injury.

It has become apparent to me that the figures from the Watson study do not appear to be accurate at all. Once practitioners learn how to identify the early signs of injury the figure often seems to leap to 90%. It is virtually a hundred percent for any practitioner who has been full time in the profession for more than 5 years. Only a very few seem to survive working full time in this profession for more than a few years without some level of injury. Armed with this experience, you can imagine that I am neither tentative nor polite about describing the current extent of injury in the bodywork profession.

APPENDIX 4: THE MECHANISM OF INJURY

So how does this injury happen? Not surprisingly, it happens in exactly the same way as it does for any other occupation or sport that requires repeated movements. The greatest irony of all is that you may even be treating clients who have these repetitive strain injuries whilst developing far worse injuries for yourself!

Newton's Third Law of Motion states that: "For every action there is an equal an opposite reaction".

This means that whenever we apply pressure to our clients, our clients apply pressure back through our *wrists*. No matter how 'aware' our movements are, no matter how well we work with energy, no matter how much organic food we eat, and no matter how well we were trained in proper stances, every ounce of force that we apply to our clients that goes through our wrists is applied back through our wrists by the client. The place these waters of force meet and collide is in your arms, fingers wrists and hands!

And these joints and bones of the hand and wrist are uniquely designed to crumble and tear for evolutionary reasons that are far too involved to get into here.

One RSI study showed that typists put 20 tonnes of pressure through their hands each day. By the same measure, I calculated that a practitioner could be putting up to 60 tonnes of pressure through their wrists in one hour. That's the weight of one British Challenger tank - every session. This explains the reason for this injury pandemic. Yet Massage is not new. So how come there is suddenly such an injury problem? What could possibly have changed to cause such an upsurge in injury? This question dominated my thinking for several years.

In terms of western massage, the sort of massage we are now giving to our clients is very different from the massage that Per Henrik Ling gave his clients 200 years ago. Modern man and woman do not come to a Massage session for the same reasons or for the same sort of touch that Ling dispensed. Massage was actually a very small part of what Ling actually did. Much of his Movement Cure was about just that – movement. He wasn't just the father of western massage and physiotherapy but also the precursor of movement approaches to healing like Feldenkreis and the Alexander technique. He was certainly quite a guy.

The massage techniques that Ling codified were only used for a few minutes in each treatment - within the context of a movement and rehabilitation therapy. The full scope of a typical Swedish Movement Cure session consisted of:

1 Active Movements: these were strengthening, stretchng and mobilisation exercises performed by the client

2 Duplication Movements: the combined work of client and practitioner, both assistive and resistive. This involved stretches and resist movements.

3 Passive Movements: performed by the practitioner or 'gymnast'. These involved joint mobilisations passive stretches and the codified massage strokes.

Of all the techniques used by Ling, it can be seen from this that *massage strokes formed less than one sixth of the Swedish Movement Cure*. For this reason, many of the early drawings of Ling's work show mobilisation and Range of Motion diagrams, as much as they show actual massage strokes.

Nor can it be said that the concerns of Modern Man and Woman resemble the concerns of Ling's clients. The massive impact that rapid social upheaval has had on the fragile human psyche as well as the daily threat of cancer, or instant nuclear or environmental contamination, is evidenced by the appearance of a veritable panoply of new psychological anxieties and neuroses. Modern clients come to massage for 50 minutes of oasis touch – 'water in the desert' touch.

Whether there any parallels for Reflexolgists has yet to be discovered. As so many Reflexologists are also Massage therapists, the removal of the hands from Massage through NO HANDS may already be contributing greatly to the job of preventing injury to Reflexologists.

APPENDIX 5: MODERN 'OASIS' TOUCH

The truth of the matter is this: Modern Man and Modern Woman come for massage to take a very different kind of cure. They come for the balm that touch can provide in times that are immensely stressful to the human psyche.

They come so that they can rebalance and self-heal. The upsurge of interest in touch therapies is growing so fast that we are almost at the point where more people go for Massage than visit their doctor! I believe that the barefoot Massage doctor is soon to become the most important member of the community.

They come to the massage therapist in the same way that a traveller in the desert comes to an oasis. Touch does so much to stimulate the natural rebalancing impulses within the body. That is why it is so hard to get them off the massage table, even when the session is over! They are still drinking thirstily at the waters of recuperation and self-healing....

The result is that techniques originally used for just a few minutes at a time are now being used repeatedly for 50-60 minutes each session. Quod Est Demonstratum?

An Injury Pandemic for the practitioners of this amazing healing art.

APPENDIX 6: ABOUT SHOES

For the major part of our species' time on this planet we have walked either barefoot or in soft shoes. The skin of the slaughtered beast would be wrapped around the foot and leg for protection. Yet still the contours of the Earth would be felt. Still the self-healing reflexes would be worked.

As civilisation developed and with it the luxury of craftsmen, so we begin to see harder soled shoes appear. In Europe, we have records of shoe-maker's guilds dating as far back as the 12th century. However, until the 19th Century, only the wealthy could afford the expensive leather shoes made by hand. Most poor folk went bare-footed or in wooden clogs. Anyone who has worn clogs for any length of time will know just how much of the foot gets stimulated by this hard and unforgiving surface! (Here in the Pennines, I can still talk to older members of the community who remember wearing clogs daily)

With the advent of mass-produced factory shoes during the late nineteenth century, more and more ordinary people had the chance to wear 'proper shoes'. The foot would find itself imprisoned from now on. And the great mass of humanity would become disconnected from the Earth. Then come the roads and the tarmac, further inhibiting any instinct that people may have had to free their feet and feel the powerful healing energies emanating from the Earth. Perhaps the most ridiculous example of this disconnection from the Earth was the stylish platform shoe of the seventies, now making an unfortunate reappearance.

Before mass-produced shoes, the shoemaker shaped the shoe around the feet. Now, people would have to fit their feet into the shoes! Having massaged over 30,000 feet so far in my lifetime, I have yet to meet one foot that even resembles its partner on the opposite leg, let alone one that resembles anyone else's foot! The guild shoemakers knew this and made small adjustments between the left and right foot of the same pair of shoes. How many of us have fitted a shoe that felt just right on one foot and noticed discomfort in the other?

Is it an 'accident' that Reflexology emerged as one of the most popular of the alternative therapies at precisely the same time as this mass imprisonment of the foot?

I sometimes wonder just how much the world would change if all shoes were banned? Imagine the return of all that *connection*. All that *earthiness*. All that *healing*…

Mmmm…. Delicious thoughts to go to sleep dreaming of…

USEFUL CONTACTS

For the work of The NO HANDS Massage Company contact:
PO BOX 57,
Hebden Bridge,
W. Yorks
Great Britain
HX7 6WW
Tel: 0870-24-30-876
www.nohandsmassage.com
enquiries@nohandsmassage.com

Association Of Reflexologists
27 Old Gloucester Street,
London WC1N 3XX,
England
Tel: 0870 5673320
Fax: 01823 336646
e-mail: info@aor.org.uk

The British Reflexology Association
Administration Office
Monks Orchard
Whitbourne
Worcester WR6 5RB
Tel: 01886-821207
Fax: 01886-822017
e-mail: bra@britreflex.co.uk

USEFUL BOOKS

The other two books in my trilogy provide valuable additional information regarding the Seven Postural Secrets as well as much detail of the Bodywork approach I espouse. Regarding Reflexology books the following list may be of interest – it is not comprehensive.

1938, Stories the Feet Can Tell by Eunice Ingham, Ingham Publishing

1945, Zone Therapy, Its Application to the Glands and Kindred Disorders, Eunice Ingham (Out of print)

1954, Stories the Feet Have Told by Eunice Ingham, Ingham Publishing

1969, Helping Yourself with Foot Reflexology by Mildred Carter, Parker Publishing

1976, Reflexology by Maybelle Segal, Wilshire Publishing

1981, The Complete Guide to Foot Reflexology by Kevin and Barbara Kunz, Prentice Hall

1981, Mirror of the Body by Anna Kaye and Don Matchen, Strawberry Press, San Francisco

1982, Reflexology Today by Doreen Bayley, Thorson's

1983, Better Health with Reflexology by Dwight C. Byers, Ingham Publishing

1983, Reflex Zone Therapy of the Feet by Hanne Marquardt, Thorson's

1985, Hand Reflexology Workbook by Kevin and Barbara Kunz, Prentice Hall

1985, Touchpoint, Reflexology the First Steps by Yvette Eastman, Ptarmigan

1986, Reflexology, A Patient's Guide by Nicola Hall, Thorson's

1987, Reflex Zone Massage by Franz Wagner, Thorson's

1987, Reflexology, the Ancient Answer to Modern Ailments by Anne Gillanders, Self-published

1993, The Complete Guide to Foot Reflexology (Revised), by Kevin and Barbara Kunz

2002, Clinical Reflexology by Mackereth and Tiran, Churchill Livingstone (this contains a chapter by the author on NO HANDS reflexology pp103-115)

WEB-SITES

Well, if you haven't seen it yet, then now is the time!
www.nohandsmassage.com

Go visit the exciting web site of the artist, John Coombes:
www.johncoombes.com

OTHER BOOKS IN THIS TRIOLOGY

The Principles and Practise of No Hands Massage – Zero Strain Bodywork

This is the book that launched the *NO HANDS* revolution to the world. Now an industry best seller, it explains the reason such a new approach was needed and how it developed. With the stunning drawings of John Coombes, it is a book that every serious Bodyworker will treasure for life. In the foreword by Leon Chaitow he describes Gerry's approach as "revolutionary, not evolutionary".

No Hands Chair Massage – conversations between Tonto and the Lone Ranger

If you have ever wanted to know why Chair Massage is so important at the same time as reading a book that will make you laugh and cry, this is it. Breaking the mould yet again, Gerry Pyves has produced a book in collaboration with David Woodhouse that will entertain and educate you like no other. Written in the form of a fascinating dialogue between these two masters of touch you will travel the Wild West of Bodywork history and climb the great mountain of Chair Massage…

To order your copies go to
www.shizen.co.uk

or write to:
Shi'Zen Publications,
PO Box 57,
Hebden Bridge,
West Yorkshire,
HX7 6WW
UK